The Luteal Phase Defect

A Physician's Story of Recurrent Miscarriages to Successful Pregnancy

JONI STUART CAZEAU
MD, CHCQM

First edition

Cover design: Jocelyn Cate, http://jocelyncate.com
Typeset / Interior design: Jocelyn Cate, http://jocelyncate.com

ISBN: 978-1-955684-10-1
Library of Congress Cataloging-in-Publication Data

Published by God's Favored Five
http://godsfavoredfive.com

~ Dedicated to ~
The Favored Five

Table of Contents

Introduction

Parenthood is one of the scariest, hardest journeys many people will ever embark upon. Most of us imagine this journey beginning with our child's first breath of air. For many this is true, but for a minority of the population, the trials of parenthood begin long before seeing the faces they so desperately long to meet.

My parents are my biggest role models in parenthood. They married young and had seven kids. They have dozens upon dozens of stories of parenting faux pas! I was baby number two, born nineteen months after my oldest sister. My mother was only twenty-one years old when I was born. Many of you have seen videos of people driving off with a baby car seat on the roof of the car. Well, I think my dad was one of the original perpetrators of this parental mistake. He tells me I was somewhere between four and six months old when he apparently strapped my big sister in the car and left the house to take us to our grandmother's house. Seconds after driving off, he heard/saw my car seat hit the ground behind the car. He tells me that he jumped out to find that he had left me on the roof of the car. When my dad tells this story, the car seat was face down in the road, but there was not a scratch on me and I just smiled at him. When my mom tells the story, I had scratches on my forehead, and I wailed all the way to my grandmother's house. Apparently my grandmother took over at that point and got me to settle down. I used to laugh when my parents told this story. Now, as a parent, I can only imagine how sick my father must have felt. I can imagine how he probably did not really breathe a sigh of relief until I started walking and talking due to the fear the fall had caused permanent damage.

My mother probably felt equally sick when she heard an electrical shock in our home in Virginia followed by a one-year-old me walking into the room she was in with a penny between two burned fingers, reporting with one word, "Burn..." In the eighties, many children lost their lives after putting metal objects into electrical sockets. We can only credit the grace of God that I walked away with only the two charred fingers. My fingers healed, much to my mother's relief!

My parents' crazy stories go on and on, including terrifying calls to meet a kid in the emergency room after an accident. This occurred at least three times for them, including a call for one of my sisters who broke her foot during a sporting practice, a brother who was hit by a car while riding a bike, and me after being the passenger of a rollover car accident going to a high school function. We all walked away with only minor injuries (except the sister with the broken foot; she limped for a while of course).

I thought my parents' anecdotes and vast experience would be enough to help guide me through parenthood. I thought they would help map out which roads to take and which roads to avoid. I knew they would have nuggets of knowledge to lend to help me raise my kids. Little did I know that my road to parenthood would involve completely uncharted territory for them and me.

Parenthood is filled with so much responsibility that the guilt asso-ciated with things that go wrong, whether in our control or not, can be overwhelming. One of the most decorated United States gymnasts is famously noted for saying that motherhood is harder than training for the Olympics! I first read the quote in 2016, a few months after the birth of my first child. All I could say was "Exactly!" I was a physician, and I had planned my pregnancy. I had made sure all of the correct pieces were in place. All I could think in my son's first six months of life was "What is going on? This is not at all what I expected." It was a million times harder than medical school or residency. I now have three children, and I still believe it to be true.

However, my road to parenthood was not as direct as many. My failures, self-doubt, and guilt as a parent began long before I ever held any of my children. I was a recurrent miscarrier. While I will likely never laugh at my miscarriages as my parents and I have laughed at many of their parental mishaps, I was able to learn from my losses, find out the medical reason for my recurrent miscarriages, and have three successful pregnancies. This is the journey I want to share with you. I pray that this blesses you and continues to move the field of medicine forward.

Preface

"When calamity comes, the wicked are brought down, but even in death the righteous seek refuge in God." (Prov. 14:32)

During medical school, I had a difficult time passing the exams required for acceptance to residency. I was a medical student in the health services scholarship program. This meant the U.S. Navy was paying for my medical school expenses as long as I met certain criteria. I actually failed the USMLE Step 1 so many times the U.S. Navy Health Professions Scholarship Program began the process of releasing me from the program. The USMLE Steps 1 and 2 are the two examinations required for entry into a physician residency program. They demonstrate a student has learned the required material from medical school. USMLE Step 1 is usually taken after completion of the second year of medical school. Step 2 is taken after completion of the third year of medical school. That typically leaves all of the fourth year of medical school to complete electives (hospital or clinic rotations of choice and usually in areas the medical student most enjoys). I attempted Step 1 after my second year of medical school and failed. I was so scared to retake Step 1 that I delayed retaking it until after my third year of medical school and failed it again. So I had not even passed Step 1 at the beginning of my fourth year of medical school.

While this may seem trivial to some readers, it was a huge faith test for me. In the month leading up to my final opportunity to take and pass the test before the U.S. Navy began the out-processing steps, I was furious with God. I felt I had faithfully served God since I was a child. I felt He had betrayed me and let me down. God had been my best friend since I was eight years old, and we had never had a fight. We had a fight then. I actually gave my best friend the silent treatment. I told Him that I would pass the test myself. I told Him He was the one allowing me to fail after I had been so faithful and put Him first in every aspect of my life.

It was the worst month of my life. Every time I got on my knees to pray, I would just cry. I couldn't bring myself to talk to Him. I couldn't listen to gospel or Christian music because it felt hypocritical. From the time I was five years old, I'd dedicated everything I had to becoming a physician. I'd known I wanted to be a physician even before I knew I wanted to serve God. I dedicated my life to God and was baptized when I was seven years old. Being a doctor was the baby I'd been carrying for over twenty years and it was dying—and my God was allowing it.

Dramatic? Maybe, but that was my mindset. On the day of the exam, I was miserable. I was bitter, resentful, and angry at my best friend. I was defiant toward my heavenly Father. I was emotionally and spiritually depleted. I walked out of the exam, sat in my car, and said, "Well, I failed that." I calmly drove back to my hotel room, and as I drove, a weight fell off of me. Once in my hotel room, I dropped to my knees, and for the first time in a month, I could pray. No more anger, just relief. After I prayed, my joy returned. I was still standing. I was still Joni, and now I was reconciled back to my God. I actually do not even have the words to describe the change that came over me. I'd failed. There were going to be consequences, but I had my best friend back and I had my joy back, and that's all that mattered.

Three weeks later I received my official notification that I had failed the examination. It was now November during my fourth year of medical school. I sat in my home and praised God. Strange, yes. I praised Him because I knew my heart had been wrong when I'd taken the last test. I told God I didn't want success without Him. I didn't want to live or move or breathe without Him. I looked at my score and said, "Okay, God, let's do this your way! I'm ready!"

The truth was, prior to this experience, I hadn't truly relied completely on God for my academic success (though I am so thankful He continued to bless me in my ignorance). I knew I was academically gifted. My brain was something I thought I could always rely on. Through these failures, I learned that GOD is who I have to rely on. I am insufficient. I am not good enough, and that's okay because with my God, all things are possible and HE is more than enough. God needed me to trust Him with what I thought was the most important part of me at that time in my life. He needed me to release what I thought was my most precious asset so He could take control and take something ordinary and make it extraordinary.

The next exam opportunity was in January. It was also my final opportunity to attempt Step 1 in time for graduation and residency placement. I proceeded with residency site visits and interviews while studying to take USMLE Step 1 and Step 2 in January at the same time. The exams were scheduled two days apart. (It is pretty unheard of to take both exams this close together.) For physicians, residents, and medical students reading this book, you understand the importance of this timeline. In January, I took both exams. Shortly after taking the exams, my medical school informed me that my tuition was due for the first semester (as I was no longer in the U.S. Navy Health Professions Scholarship Program, the U.S. Navy had not paid my tuition), and if I did not pay it by February 15, I would not be able to continue my education.

One day in early February, I was sitting in our medical school computer lab and an email popped up stating my test scores were available to view. With my heart pounding, I opened the link and saw my USMLE Step 1 score and PASS, followed by my USMLE Step 2 score and PASS. I sat there and cried and praised my God. Then God proceeded to truly show off.

Prior to passing my USMLE exams, I had the opportunity to complete a Family Medicine elective rotation at Naval Hospital Pensacola in Florida. I fell in love with the program, the city, and the people in the program. This program was my first choice for residency training. At my exit interview, the program director saw that I had not passed my exams. He looked at my academic transcript and my test scores. He told me that my transcript showed that I knew the material. He then gave me a certified military captain motivational speech for which I will be forever grateful. I separated from the military prior to reaching the rank of a captain, so I think I missed out on the course on how to give a motivational speech to motivate sailors to go charging full speed into unwinnable battles and come out victorious, but I really walked out of his office ready to storm the mountain called USMLE! He told me the out-processing from the Navy would begin but to contact him the moment I passed the exams.

Upon receiving my passing scores, I immediately emailed the captain at the Family Medicine residency program in Pensacola, Florida. I notified him that I had passed both exams and forwarded my test results to him. The captain emailed me back and said congratulations. He asked if I still wanted to come to Naval Hospital Pensacola for residency training. I told him yes, absolutely. In the next week, I was reinstated into the U.S. Navy Health Professions Scholarship Program. My tuition was paid in full for the first and second semesters of my fourth year of medical school, *and* I received an acceptance letter to my first choice for residency! The military releases residency match results before civilian matches are released. While I was late for the military match release date, I was matched for residency before the civilian match day.

This experience taught me that all things are possible with God, that I can't win without Him, and that I can't lose with Him. It also taught me that I am His. He will never leave me nor forsake me. I am miserable without Him, and nothing is worse for me than *not* being with God. I knew I would never give God the silent treatment again. When trials came and when in the fire, I would run to and stick closer to God. That was the only choice for me. I graduated on time from medical school in 2008 and began my active duty service as a Family Medicine resident in Pensacola, Florida. Little did I know that it would be this trial that would prepare me to not let go of God's hand through the hardest battle of my life: recurrent miscarriages.

Chapter One: Happy Newlywed News

Notable Historic Events Occurring on September 11:

1839 – 1st Canadian track & field meet held (Caer Howell Grounds)

1853 – 1st electric telegraph used (Merchant's Exchange to Pt Lobos)

1875 – 1st newspaper cartoon strip

1889 – Start of Sherlock Holmes' adventure "Crooked Man" (BG)

1918 – Boston Red Sox beat Chicago Cubs 4 games to 2 in 15th World Series

1926 – U.S. defeats France for their 7th straight Davis Cup championship

1927 – Babe Ruth hits 50th of 60 homers

1928 – Ty Cobb's last hitting appearance, pops out against Yankees 1930 – Stromboli volcano (Sicily) throws 2-ton basaltic rocks 2 miles 1935 – U.S. captures Davis Cup for 7th straight year

1941 – Construction of the Pentagon begins (completed January 15, 1943)

1951 – Florence Chadwick becomes 1st woman to swim English Channel from England to France. It takes 16 hours, 19 minutes.

1954 – 1st Miss America TV broadcast

1960 – 17th Olympic Games close in Rome, Italy

1962 – Beatles cut "Love Me Do" and "P.S. I Love You" with Andy

White on drums

1962 – Drummer Ringo Starr replaces Pete Best of the Beatles

1985 – Flyby of Comet Giacobini-Zinner

1998 – Opening ceremony for the 1998 Commonwealth Games in Kuala Lumpur, Malaysia. Malaysia is the first Asian country to host the games.

2014 – **Estimated due date of Jean and Joni Cazeau's first child**

Greg and I were married in May of 2013. In January of 2014, I gave this list of notable events in world history to my husband one day after he returned home from work to announce we were pregnant with our first child. We were six months into our marriage. This was our dream come true! We were expecting the first addition to our family!

No Heartbeat

"Ughp, there's no heartbeat," the ultrasound tech stated. My mind froze as I frantically attempted to grasp the meaning of those four words, but I could not. My husband and I were in the room with the ultrasound technician. It was our second ultrasound early in our pregnancy. The initial ultrasound of our first baby, at six weeks gestation, had shown a slower than desired heart rate at ninety-five beats per minute. This ultrasound was a follow-up, hoping to see the heart rate increase to the expected range. I was eight weeks pregnant and still filled with all of the anticipation and hope of an expecting mom. Those were the last words on earth I would have expected to hear.

Now, don't get me wrong; I am a family medicine physician. I definitely understood the meaning of the words spoken by the ultrasound technician in a medical sense. However, in that moment, my mind could not make the turn as to how that could pertain to my baby's heartbeat. My only thoughts were "She's wrong and incompetent. I need a doctor. The doctor will find the heartbeat." I'd walked into the office with only the expectation of hearing a healthy heartbeat for our baby. No other outcome had even crossed my mind. I knew without question that God loved me and that reproduction was in His will. The Bible says, "Be fruitful and multiply." Why would the technician even say something like that? Those horrible words were not in line with anything in my life. I didn't want her to say anything else to us. The technician was ruining *everything.*

I am going to pause here because this book is intended to serve as a tool for education, healing, encouragement, and building of your faith in the face of loss. If you are reading this book, you may have suffered a similar loss. This book may be the first book you picked up after your loss or the thirtieth book you are reading. Your loss may be recent, or some time may have passed. If you've accessed other resources during your search for healing and restoration, you may have been introduced to the five stages of grief. The purpose of this book is not to dwell on the stages of grief, but I will mention them here because you may have noticed above that I quickly displayed two of the five stages, denial and anger. I wanted to point out the anger because I directed my initial anger toward the poor technician. At that moment, she was enemy number one. I actually placed my anger on the poor technician for quite some time. As a spoiler alert, from the book title, you can gather that this would not be the last time I would be told my expected baby did not have a heartbeat. Oddly enough, this technician would be the one performing most of my ultrasounds for all five of my pregnancies.

The technician told me that she would let my doctor know what was going on, and she finally stepped out of the room. I looked at my husband. He asked me what it meant. He is not in the medical field, so he often relies on me to provide perspective to the medical information provided during our medical encounters. I had to hang on to hope, so I told him that I would not believe anything the technician said. From my experience, physicians were the ones who read ultrasounds, not technicians. We got dressed and were ushered to our doctor's examination room.

Our doctor proceeded to repeat the technician's findings. It was so strange. I had been in her position before, having to share devastating news with a patient or family members. I could have recited the speech to myself. I could recognize the skill and choice of words, the body positioning. The clinician in me actually appreciated her skill with telling me I'd just lost my child. I recognized her intentional pauses to try to allow my mind to catch up with the information she was providing.

As an objective physician, I did have to give her great credit for the way she did her job that day. As a mother, it didn't matter what she said. My mind was gone. I'd somehow killed my baby. What had I done wrong? Did my baby feel anything as its heart stopped beating? What was their brief life like? Did they know they were loved, cherished, and wanted? As a physician, I knew the standard answers. I'd also reassured devastated mothers in the past. In that moment, I realized my reassurance to my patients was likely not reassuring at all.

For physicians or physicians-in-training reading this, please note, in the moment, our words to our patients may be falling quite flat. I still appreciated the words because they showed my doctor was trying and she cared. An important lesson I'd also learned during my residency training was that no two patients are the same, and reactions to such news are beyond unpredictable. I've experienced responses on the complete opposite ends of the spectrum when sharing devastating information with patients. I actually sat on the table that day as my doctor spoke to me and flashed back to some of the responses from my patients in such moments. Some patients may just want to leave the office as soon as possible and may not want to hear our words immediately. Some may need all of those words while they begin processing their situation. I may have been right in the middle. I wanted to get out to process on my own, but I was frozen, stuck. The fact that she kept talking for a bit gave my brain the opportunity to tell the rest of me that I had to move.

Honestly, after leaving the office, the rest is a blur. It is amazing how the office visit is imprinted in my brain forever. Physicians, training physicians, I know we have heard this a million times, but I have to say it again: What we say and do matters. We are truly with our patients through their highest and lowest moments, with their utmost trust and confidence that we have the solution to their problems. I know we know this. I know it has been ingrained in us. However, some things are worth saying again, and again, and again. What we say and do matters. The weight of a physician is heavy at times. It is hard to shoulder all of the expectations and emotions at times. However, as a patient, I am so thankful and appreciative for the providers who walked through this journey with me because what we do matters and they did their jobs well!

After leaving my doctor's office, we had to tell all of our close friends and family that we were no longer expecting and had suffered a mis-carriage. Having to repeat the news and experience their reactions was horrible. Physician colleagues, as hard as it is to live through these moments with our patients, we are truly better in these moments than 99% of everyone else they will encounter. The conversations they have with us will likely be the least awkward, most comforting, and among the most enlightening our patients will have during these times. While we feel we do not have all of the right words and we sometimes stick our foot in our mouths, the rest of the world is even less equipped to deal with comforting our patients after a loss than we are. Oddly enough, only two people said the right thing immediately after our miscarriage, and one of them was my husband. Pretty much everyone else said the wrong thing and then did not want to talk about it anymore. While my loved ones' words fell flat during this time, I still truly appreciated and needed their efforts and love.

Over the next few days and weeks, I prayed *a lot*. I also searched for self-help books and tools for grief after a miscarriage. I was actually surprised by the resources I found. As a Christian physician/scientist, prayer and research are my safe places, my go-tos when I am lost and do not know what to do. I know that those two strategies will give me the answers I need. I remember having a sadness, but also peace and optimism. I knew God loved me. I knew that He would never leave me nor forsake me. I had all of the faith in the world that all things would work out for my good. I remember my pastor at the time even thinking I was in denial and that I was not allowing myself to process and address my loss because I just kept going. I kept serving. I appeared unfazed. I wasn't unfazed, but I kept praying and reading the Word of God. I kept building my faith with faith scriptures and the promises of God. I had my faith in God, and that was enough at that time to keep me going.

As a physician, I also knew the miscarriage statistics. Approximately ten percent of clinically known first trimester pregnancies end in miscarriage. Depending on what source we use, the percentage increases to as high as thirty percent when including non-clinically known pregnancies. I also knew that most women go on to have normal pregnancies after a miscarriage. After suffering my first miscarriage, the statistics were encouraging to me because I believed it was not completely abnormal to suffer a miscarriage, and I believed I would go on to have successful pregnancies. I just knew God would give me the desires of my heart.

Faith Corner

Prayer for Medical Providers:
    Heavenly Father,
    Thank you so much for the awesome privilege of being an extension

of your healing hand. Thank you for the trust that your children and my patients put in me every day to care for them. Give me the wisdom and medical knowledge I need to treat your children, heavenly Father. Make me take every complaint, every issue seriously. Anoint my mind and hands to heal according to your Word. Give me the patience, compassion, and love needed to listen, treat, and minister as you would have me to do. Let me speak words of life, encouragement, and truth in love to every patient. Help me to realize that I am the front line, and sometimes the only line, my patients have to truthfully share their medical issues. Give me the strength to bear their burdens when needed and to release them to you, knowing that you are a good God who loves every one of your children. Thank you for the opportunity to serve you by serving them! Amen.

For Women:

Heavenly Father,

I give you glory today and forevermore. All glory belongs to you, Daddy. When I am rejoicing, I give you glory, and when I am hurting, I still give you glory. As long as I have breath in my lungs, I will give you glory, my God. Lord, I am putting my trust in you right now that you will heal my heart. Heal my body. Heal my soul. Heal my spirit. Heal me, Lord. I cannot breathe without you. I cannot move without you. You are my life. You are my lifeline. I put my hope, trust, and faith in you, for it is in you that I live and move and have my being. Minister to my mind now. Open my ears to hear and my heart and soul to receive what you would have me to receive in these pages so that I walk daily in the confidence that your Word is true, complete, and for ME! I have the victory in you. You have promised to never leave me nor forsake me. The fact that I am reading this book now is proof that you are still speaking and ministering to me. Don't let me miss anything that you have for me. I receive, I receive, I receive, I receive! Thank you for loving me. Thank you for loving me.

Thank you for loving me. Thank you for the healing even now! I love you, Daddy! Amen.

Key Scriptures:

Psalm 107:19–20

Then they cry unto the LORD in their trouble, and he saveth them out of their distresses. He sent his word, and healed them, and delivered them from their destructions.

Psalm 103:1–5

Bless the LORD, O my soul: and all that is within me, bless his holy name. Bless the LORD, O my soul, and forget not all his benefits: Who forgiveth all thine iniquities; who healeth all thy diseases; Who redeemeth thy life from destruction; who crowneth thee with lovingkindness and tender mercies; Who satisfieth thy mouth with good things; so that thy youth is renewed like the eagle's.

Hebrews 10:35–37

Cast not away therefore your confidence, which hath great recompence of reward. For ye have need of patience, that, after ye have done the will of God, ye might receive the promise. For yet a little while, and he that shall come will come, and will not tarry.

Chapter Two: Nine Months Later

Our first baby's due date was September 11, 2014. I found out we were pregnant again the same month our first baby would have been born. Wow! My thought was "God is amazing! This has to be God!" This time, we did not run out and tell everyone. We decided we would wait until our first ultrasound or the end of the first trimester because telling people we were no longer pregnant was an absolutely horrible experience that we did not want to risk going through again. We only told people who needed to know that we were pregnant again. We kept our wonderful, joyous news a special secret between us and anticipated the moment we could share our news with everyone.

We had our first ultrasound on October 24, 2014, and it was normal. Our baby was measuring six weeks and three days gestational age. We had our initial obstetric evaluation on November 5, 2014. Everything was looking great. Two days later that changed.

The Friday before Veteran's Day, my husband and I were eating at TGI Fridays. I went to the restroom and noticed a small amount of light pink blood in my undergarments. Anyone that has experienced a trauma more than once understands the sickening dread and fear that comes when you feel the trauma reoccurring. I tried to maintain my composure and faith as I walked back out to the table. My mind was numb, but I didn't want to make a scene at dinner. I made it through dinner and told my husband of my findings when we got to the car.

We called our doctor. The on-call physician provided the counseling I knew all too well. A little spotting can be normal in the first trimester of pregnancy. If it increased or continued, go to the emergency room over the weekend. Call Monday to get an ultrasound. I had no further bleeding. We were scheduled for an ultrasound the following week. The same ultrasound technician performed our ultrasound. She relayed to us that there was, again, no heartbeat. She told us, by the measurements, it appeared as though our baby died at about seven weeks gestational age. This baby had been the same age as our first baby. This time, there was no denial, anger, or bargaining, just sadness. This time I did not just keep moving. This time I did not take our loss on the chin. Statistics could not encourage me. I was beyond the encouraging statistics. I now knew this was not a coincidence. There was something wrong with me, and I was depressed.

I had never been depressed before. I am typically an extremely positive and hopeful person, so this was new. As a clinician, I kept wondering at what point I needed clinical help. Spoiler alert: I actually ended up seeing a psychologist after the birth of my first child for therapy for a military sexual trauma that occurred in 2012. However, at the time of my miscarriage, I dug and dug for resources on coping after a miscarriage. I definitely kept praying and seeking God. I also became fixated on finding out what went wrong. My prayer became "God, please help me find out what is wrong with me and fix it." In my mind, if I could fix the problem, the depression would end.

After our second miscarriage, I remember sitting in church services numb. I literally remember feeling like I had been in a horrible accident, like a car crash or something equivalent, and that I was going in and out of consciousness as medical personnel performed life-saving care and procedures. Except the medical personnel were ministering angels, and God was the head of the team. Though I may never be able to accurately articulate the experience, each time I sat in the church pews, my numb physician brain literally felt myself undergoing spiritual surgery. During services, I felt like I was under anesthesia. I don't think I ever really followed what was going on in the service. I couldn't focus. Even during praise and worship, when I opened my mouth to sing, I only wanted to cry, so I did not sing. But I knew I was where I needed to be, so I made sure I was in attendance. I knew the only person who could heal me physically, mentally, emotionally, and spiritually was God, and I was definitely broken. I would feel the ministering angels around me as God performed surgery...and I just sat. I sometimes wondered if I was feeling something similar to Hannah in 1 Samuel 1:10–15.

[10] *In her deep anguish Hannah prayed to the LORD, weeping bitterly.* [11] *And she made a vow, saying, "LORD Almighty, if you will only look on your servant's misery and remember me, and not forget your servant but give her a son, then I will give him to the LORD for all the days of his life, and no razor will ever be used on his head."*

[12] *As she kept on praying to the LORD, Eli observed her mouth.* [13] *Hannah was praying in her heart, and her lips were moving but her voice was not heard. Eli thought she was drunk* [14] *and said to her, "How long are you going to stay drunk? Put away your wine."*

[15] *"Not so, my lord," Hannah replied, "I am a woman who is deeply troubled. I have not been drinking wine or beer; I was pouring out my soul to the LORD.* [16] *Do not take your servant for a wicked woman; I have been praying here out of my great anguish and grief."*

From previous experiences, there was no way I was going to run from God. I knew that stepping away from God would be instant death in this situation. I had suffered substantial injuries, and my physician brain categorized myself as a level one trauma patient. I knew only one physician skilled enough to treat my injuries: God. I didn't know how

He was going to do it. I had no answers. The only thing I knew for sure: Do not step away, or I will surely die.

I include this in this book because the church is often referred to as God's hospital. It was truly a hospital for me during my time of injury and healing. I can't tell you that every church service I attended during this time was hugely impactful or that there was some big breakthrough moment. I kept recalling previous patient histories requiring numerous surgeries following a traumatic event. I remembered seeing "before" pictures of mangled tissue followed by "after" pictures 300 surgeries later with reconstructed, fully functional body parts. It hadn't been one surgery that made the difference for those patients but the combined effects of each surgery. I remembered seeing the surgical planning, mapping, and integration of multiple surgical specialties and nonsurgical specialties. I remembered seeing success stories with people taking first steps in physical therapy and gripping balls in occupational therapy. I felt that although I couldn't see or feel the procedures occurring, God was working hard to repair my mangled body, soul, and spirit. I even remember the first time I laughed and how awkward it felt (and how guilty I felt for being able to laugh). I actually had to learn to laugh again...and then how to do it without feeling guilty. Slowly but surely, I began to see the return of Joni.

Now, what was so broken after the second miscarriage? I believe there were multiple issues. I believe I was physically and emotionally depleted due to two miscarriages in nine months. Physically, I believe that my body was undergoing significant hormonal changes (naturally), but also I believe my body felt the losses and knew that death had occurred. Science has shown that fetomaternal transfer probably occurs in all pregnancies. Cells from the fetus enter the mother's body, where they become a part of her tissues. After my second miscarriage, I actually felt like part of me died—not that something inside of me had died but that my own personal body had experienced death. Had cells transferred from my babies to me, and did that genetic material recognize that a part of it had died? Also, both of my miscarriages were considered missed abortions. That means the babies actually died inside my body. Afterward, when my body did not naturally stop trying to support a pregnancy, I had to take a medication to let it know I was no longer pregnant. In the days after their deaths, in which I waited for my body to undergo a natural abortion, was a lot of genetic tissue from my babies transferred to me? Is that why I felt the second death so deeply? I will never know, but somehow I felt a loss I'd never felt before and may never have the words to fully explain.

I believe the biggest issue was that I lost hope. The Bible says in Proverbs 18:14, "The spirit of a man will sustain his infirmity; but a wounded spirit who can bear?" I no longer believed I could have a successful pregnancy unless God healed me. The problem with this was that other than knowing I was barren, I didn't know what healing I needed in order to have a successful pregnancy. Not knowing what to do or how to fix the problem was brutal. I didn't know what I should be praying to God about. What could I ask Him to fix?

Some may be wondering if I was angry with God after my miscarriages. Actually, no. Now, don't get me wrong. I definitely asked why. But I vehemently cast down any semblance of anger or division with God. Someone reading this book may be angry with God right now while going through their situation. I've gone down the "angry with God" road before, and it did not work (remember my medical school story?). The one month during medical school in which I was angry with God ended up being the worst month of my life, and I didn't even get the results I wanted when I tried to go out on my own. If I couldn't even pass a test on my own, there was no way I was ever going to try to have a baby on my own. Even with the pain of my miscarriages and as damaged as I felt, I still felt better going through this with God than I did during that month so long ago during my medical school experience. I was unequivocally going to fail or succeed *with* God.

I actually believe that is why God allowed me to go through my trials in medical school—so that when true physical death occurred in my life, I would not turn away from Him in my darkest hour. If I am speaking to you right now, turn and run to your heavenly Father. He is right there with you, and the burden that will come off of you when you grab His hand will be amazing. If you get nothing from this book, get this: Grab ahold of God's hand, and DO NOT LET GO.

Faith Corner

For Medical Providers:

Dear Lord,

My patients are hurting. I need your anointing, heavenly Father. Please anoint me to minister to the hurting and downtrodden. Help me to see the mental, emotional, and spiritual injuries and not just the physical. When I recognize nonphysical injuries, give me wisdom to know how to approach each subject as you would have me to do. Even when I am frustrated or behind schedule, help me to take a breath and be a conduit of your love. I ask that you take care of my schedule, my home life, my children, my spouse, my finances, and my personal issues so that I can focus on ministering effectively to treat my hurting and injured patients. Let them see you in me. Let them walk away from an encounter with me knowing that you have ministered to them. Knowing that you are answering their prayers. Knowing that you are still in control. Give me an ear to hear you as I listen to them so I know what actions to take on their behalf. Anoint my mind with new inventions, ideas, and treatments on their behalf. Anoint my mouth that I will say exactly what you would have me to say. I give you glory even now for the spirits you are lifting and the lives you will impact through my obedience and submission to you! It is in your holy and matchless name I pray! Amen!

For Women:

Daddy,

I am hurt. I am injured. I am hurting. I need your healing. I need your strength. I need your wisdom. Like the "Footprints in the Sand" poem, I need you to carry me right now. Do for me in this season what only you can do. Be my Father, be my protector, be my healer, be my doctor, be my comforter, be my strength. God, only you know. Only you know. You know how I feel. You know what I need. You know who I need. While I never expected this, this did not surprise you. You knew that this moment would come. You know the end from the beginning. You knew I'd be praying to you today. You knew that my heart would be broken. You knew that my spirit would be broken. You knew that I would not be able to go on without you. Thank you! Thank you for knowing. Thank you for being all-knowing. Thank you for knowing me. Thank you for knowing this day would come, and thank you for promising never to leave me nor forsake me. Thank you that while I do not know what to say, do, or think, you are in control. You know the end from the beginning. Your Word says that you will not put more on us than we can bear. If you brought me to it, you will bring me through it. You are my redeemer. You will give me joy for my pain. I believe you will make everything work out for my good. I feel like I am in the fire, but I know that you are with me. Yea, though I walk through the valley of the shadow of death, you are with me. I know that if you are with me, I will be victorious. If it takes me quoting your Word every second of every day, I will walk through this valley knowing you are with me. My spirit will not die. My body will not die. I will not die. My strength comes from the Lord, and I will be victorious. I will live through this. I will live. I thank you in advance for the victory. I speak victory. I proclaim victory. I speak victory. I proclaim victory in my life. I am your child. Thank you for being my faithful father. It is in your name I pray. Amen.

Key Scriptures:

Psalm 34:18

The LORD is near to the broken hearted. And He saves those who are crushed in the spirit.

Psalm 23

The LORD is my shepherd, I shall not want. He maketh me to lie down in green pastures; he leadeth me beside the still waters. He restoreth my soul; he leadeth me in the paths of righteousness for his name's sake. Yea, though I walk through the valley of the shadow of death, I will fear no evil, for you art with me; thy rod and thy staff they comfort me. Thou preparest a table before me in the presence of mine enemies; thou anointest my head with oil; my cup runneth over. Surely goodness and mercy shall follow me all the days of my life and I will dwell in the house of the LORD forever.

Psalm 118:16−17

The right hand of the LORD is exalted: the right hand of the LORD doeth valiantly. I shall not die, but live, and declare the works of the LORD.

Jeremiah 31:13−14

...I will turn their mourning into joy; I will comfort them, and give them gladness for sorrow...and my people shall be satisfied with my goodness, declares the LORD.

Psalm 107:1−5,

O give thanks unto the LORD, for he is good: for his mercy endureth forever. Let the redeemed of the LORD say so, whom he hath redeemed from the hand of the enemy; And gathered them out of the lands, from the east, and from the west, from the north, and from the south. They wandered in the wilderness in a solitary way; they found no city to dwell in. Hungry and thirsty, their soul fainted in them. Then they cried unto the LORD in their trouble, and he delivered them out of their distresses.

Chapter Three: My Best Friend

For women who are not married or who do not have a husband or a partner to walk with through this trial, God has promised never to leave us or forsake us. Hebrews 13:5—6 reminds us, "...for he hath said, I will never leave thee, nor forsake thee. So that we may boldly say, The Lord is my helper, and I will not fear what man shall do unto me." Yes, going through such personal trials can be and is often lonely, but we are never alone. The moment we truly grasp that revelation, we can grab the hand of our Lord and Savior, Jesus Christ. Through many of my trials, the only thing I could do was not let go of my heavenly Father's hand. He is enough—period.

Let's actually take a look at the verses leading up to God telling us He will never leave us nor forsake us in Hebrews 13:1—6:

Let brotherly love continue. Be not forgetful to entertain strangers: for thereby some have entertained angels unawares. Remember them that are in bonds, as bound with them; and them which suffer adversity, as being yourselves also in the body. Marriage is honourable in all, and the bed undefiled: but whoremongers and adulterers God will judge. Let your conversation be without covetousness; and be content with such things as ye have: for he hath said, I will never leave thee, nor forsake thee. So that we may boldly say, The Lord is my helper, and I will not fear what man shall do unto me.

This scripture is talking about how we should love our fellow man, right? It starts with brotherly love and then even goes into marriage. Right after speaking about marriage, it instructs us to speak without covetousness. God knows the discussion of love and marriage leads to strong emotions. He knows it is so easy to get "stuck" in the marriage aspect of "the conversation" and what we do or don't have as it relates to marriage. So He tells us to focus on what we do have when these moments come up. Then he waves His hand wildly and says, "You have ME!" He goes on to explain that He will never leave us or forsake us. My God is better than a spouse. He is more faithful than a spouse, more loving than spouse, and more patient than a spouse. He is everything to me. The amazing thing is, He can be everything to all of us. This scripture is appropriate here because my testimony involves my husband. God knows every woman's situation is different. No matter what your situation, He has promised never to leave you or forsake you. So, yes, every lady reading this book can go through this process with their best friend. We just have to choose to let Him in.

When speaking about our miscarriages, I say "our" and "we." My husband and I got pregnant together. We rejoiced together. We planned and dreamed together. We lost together. While I was praying and researching, he was praying and researching. He amazed me by coming to me with wonderful things to do to help us heal.

I'd made a practice of writing poems for my husband on special occasions, which started while we were dating. I actually wrote a poem to announce our first pregnancy to him. (I gave it to him with the list of notable events.) My husband is a writer as well, and he also wrote for me on special occasions. I believe the most cathartic moment for me was when he shared the poem he wrote for our baby after we miscarried. I'd written about our baby's conception. He wrote about our baby's short but loved life.

For married women who are reading this book and suffering through a miscarriage, please know you are not alone. God gave us someone to walk through these trials with. My husband lost just as much as I did. My husband likely felt more helpless than I did. As a protector, he is supposed to protect his wife and his offspring. As sad as I was, I was still able to process this much. It may have been because I'd seen many couples during medical trials and witnessed the distress, fear, and helplessness of husbands in the face of such events. I'd seen husbands struggle as we urgently transitioned laboring wives to emergent cesareans. I'd heard the fear and helplessness in their voices as they frantically asked what they should or could do. I'd seen them doing everything and anything medical providers requested for their wives in those precarious moments. I'd seen the love and tenderness while awaiting the arrival of their baby and the joy, relief, and pride once their loved ones were safely in their arms. I knew I was not alone. I would implore wives, please don't isolate yourself from your husband when you are suffering through a miscarriage.

This is where I think God's order is perfect. I was broken and severely injured. I needed someone to lean on, cry on, and make me feel safe. I did just that. I pulled my husband closer and leaned on him, mostly because I honestly could not have stood on my own. My husband did just what he was designed to do; he protected me. Now, is there a perfect formula for this? No. You know your husband and yourself. For me, if my husband offered to do something or recommended we do something, I did it. I honestly did not have the will or energy to object. His stepping in was definitely ordained and orchestrated by God.

Living life after miscarriages was new terrain for both of us. I allowed him to navigate whenever he took the helm. It got to the point I felt he was so in tune with me that when we were in public settings, he could read my face or my body language and would gently whisk me away. I didn't have to say a word or even give him a look. He just knew. Laughingly, now I wonder just how horrible I looked for him to be so perceptive, but I truly believe God gave him a special anointing, discernment, and wisdom as my husband during that time.

I don't know how much support I was for him. He might have to write his own book for husbands where he shares how he healed. From the wife's perspective, I leaned on him and told him how grateful I was for everything he was doing. I was also honest about how I was feeling about our miscarriages. I did not keep it from him. I don't think I could have kept it from him. I needed to talk about our miscarriages and my feelings with someone for some sort of release. I had to share my disappointment, fear, resolve, and pain. No one could understand or know what I was feeling better than he could. Our miscarriages actually brought us closer together. Only we knew our suffering, our faith, and our love for each other and our babies in heaven.

I found that outside of my physicians, there really was no one else in my inner circle to talk to about our miscarriages. It was a very lonely place. I felt my family was extremely awkward. I have four sisters and two brothers. In the past, at least one of them was useful for each particular trial I'd faced. I also historically leaned heavily on my parents. None of the closest members of my support system could help. They didn't have a reference point at that time in their lives. I do have to say, my dad is very gifted at knowing what to say to his kids in times of need. He did not disappoint after our first miscarriage and I truly appreciated his words, but I could not solely live and continue to function off of one conversation. I needed my husband, and he was willing, called, appointed, and anointed for the task.

While we did not announce our second pregnancy, we did have to tell our families about our second miscarriage because the miscarriage happened right before Thanksgiving. We had missed abortions, which meant the baby was still in my uterus but was no longer living. It can take your body a while to realize that it is no longer pregnant. I had the choice to use medications to help my body release everything in my uterus, or I could wait to see if my body went through the process without assistance. With both of my miscarriages, I waited but ultimately ended up requiring assistance. I required medication and procedural assistance. As you can imagine, this process can take weeks. I was diagnosed with a missed abortion on November 11, 2014. The process of completing the miscarriage took through the week of Thanksgiving, and I was still bleeding during the holiday. I was clearly out of it physically, emotionally, and mentally. There was no way to hide it. We had to let them know we were grieving and were not our usual selves.

We went home to Virginia for Christmas, and my parents and siblings didn't know how to treat me. They didn't know what to say. Rightfully so, my thoughts were that we should be celebrating Christmas with our first baby in our arms, and we'd just suffered a second insult with the loss of our second baby. I didn't share those thoughts with my family, but I did share them with the one person I knew was thinking and feeling the same thing. Again, I don't know how he did it, but even in his injured state, he knew exactly what to say to get us through our first Christmas dealing with loss.

After Christmas, my husband took me to New Orleans, Louisiana, to bring in the New Year. He took me to my home church and my spiritual parents, Bishop Paul S. Morton and Pastor Debra B. Morton. He took me somewhere everyone knew me but they did not know about my miscarriages. It was great. My church family loved on me and encouraged me without even knowing what we were going through! It was a great way to say goodbye to the hardest year of my life with people who loved me and I loved so dearly, who didn't look at me with pity and sorrow. I do have to add here that of course I shared the news of my miscarriages with Pastor D. I'd actually talked with her after the first miscarriage. God used her awesomely months before our December trip to speak into my life. I am so thankful that God knows exactly what we need and when we need it and that He is always faithful.

When my husband and I returned from New Orleans, I felt I had new life and new fight in me. The despair was there, but a glimmer of hope had returned and that was enough. It just takes faith the size of a mustard seed, and I had gotten it. "If ye have faith as a grain of mustard seed, ye shall say unto this mountain, remove hence to yonder place; and it shall remove; and nothing shall be impossible to you" (Matt. 17:20).

Faith Corner

Prayer for Women:

Heavenly Father,

Thank you for not making me go through this alone, because YOU are ALWAYS with me. Even when I can't feel you. Even when I am angry or hurt, you have promised never to leave me nor forsake me. Daddy, show me the people in my life who can share with me during this time. Give me medical providers of faith who can speak life and encouragement. Anoint my pastors to speak words of wisdom and life. Give me the strength and humility to allow others to help me through this time. Anoint my friends and family to speak godly words. Anoint their mouths, Heavenly Father, that they will not speak death, fear, or any other negative word that is contrary to your Word and will for my life. Give them the mind of Christ that they may be a blessing in thought and deed to me. Give them witty ideas to minister to my spirit. Surround me with godly love and support. Remove me and isolate me when needed to protect my mind and spirit. For I know that we do not wrestle against flesh and blood but against spirits and principalities and wickedness in high places. Make my spirit man to stand victorious. Strengthen, heal, repair my spirit man so I may fight and win the true battle. I humbly lean on you, Daddy and I give you all the glory and praise even now because victory is inevitable. You are MY God, who has never lost a battle. Glory! Thank you for knowing what to say to minister to me. You are my strengthener! You are my rock, the rock of my salvation. Glory to your name. Amen, amen, amen!

Prayer for Medical Providers:

Dear Lord,

Thank you for the trust you put in me every day to minister to your children. I know that my patients are hurting physically, mentally, emotionally, and spiritually. I thank you for the skills, gifts, and talents you have given me to be a minister of health and healing. Anoint me afresh to minister to your children's spirit even as I minister to them physically. Give me godly wisdom and insight to speak life where they are feeling death and despair. Give me godly words that will allow them to know you are with them and that with you, *all* things are possible—no matter what medical information I have to share with them. Let my patients hear you in the words that I speak. Help me to ask the right questions and to slow down and listen to you while I am with my patients so I may be the minister of health you have called me to be. This is an awesome responsibility. Thank you for trusting me. Help me to walk boldly in the position and authority you have given me. I glorify you now for the testimonies and lives that will be touched. It is in your name I pray. Amen!

Key Scriptures:

Genesis 25:21

And Isaac entreated the LORD for his wife, because she was barren: and the LORD was entreated of him, and Rebekah his wife conceived.

Deuteronomy 31:6

Be strong and of a good courage, fear not, nor be afraid of them: for the LORD thy God, he it is that doth go with thee; he will not fail thee, nor forsake thee.

Psalm 89:24, 26

But my faithfulness and my mercy shall be with him: and in my name shall his horn be exalted. He shall cry unto me, Thou art my father, my God, and the rock of my salvation.

Ephesians 6:11–13

Put on the whole armour of God, that ye may be able to stand against the wiles of the devil. For we wrestle not against flesh and blood, but against principalities, against powers, against the rulers of the darkness of this world, against spiritual wickedness in high places. Wherefore take unto you the whole armour of God, that ye may be able to withstand in the evil day, and having done all, to stand.

Chapter Four: Finding and Fixing the Problem

The Science of It All

After our second miscarriage, I became fixated on researching recurrent first trimester miscarriages to find out what was wrong with me. I could not focus on anything else. I promised that my first two babies' lives would not be in vain. I researched and researched. I read many online women's blogs and forum posts discussing recurrent miscarriages. I found a theme that appeared similar to my own. I'd found my answer, and I will be forever grateful to the women who selflessly and openly shared their stories in these blogs to help others. These women used the term luteal phase defect. Interestingly enough, even as a physician, I had never heard of this term related to miscarriages.

My husband and I met with our obstetrician and I told her I thought I had a luteal phase defect. I told her this in May of 2015. I add the year here because it is now 2022 and a luteal phase defect is still not widely accepted as a cause of recurrent miscarriage in women. According to an article on recurrent pregnancy loss, on Uptodate.com,

A 2015 Committee Opinion released by the American Society for Reproductive Medicine concluded that "there is no reproducible, pathophysiologically relevant, and clinically practical standard to diagnose luteal phase deficiency and distinguish fertile from infertile women." The committee concluded that luteal phase deficiency as an independent cause of infertility has not been proven. We do not perform luteal phase testing.[1]

Okay, let me pause here. For physicians and those in the medical profession, some may already be calling a "flag on the play." As I stated above, I had never even heard of the term luteal phase defect in 2015. The key to the luteal phase defect is a lack of the production of progesterone during early pregnancy. So whether I use the term luteal phase defect or progesterone deficiency, the outcome is the same: recurrent first trimester miscarriage. As this is an area in which more research is needed, I ask that we focus on the science at this time. Though my symptoms aligned highly with those described in the luteal phase defect diagnosis, my medical evaluation clearly demonstrated a progesterone deficiency and I was diagnosed with and treated for "progesterone deficiency." Therefore, I will use the term progesterone deficiency as my personal diagnosis. A luteal phase defect would be considered a potential cause of progesterone deficiency.

So let's talk science (probably my third love in life...God, family, science)! Progesterone is the hormone required for successful implantation and sustainment of pregnancy before the placenta is formed. Wow! That being said, progesterone is the most important hormone in pregnancy! Let's go further to the luteal phase defect aspect. The corpus luteum is a hormone-secreting structure that develops in an ovary after an egg has been released and degenerates after a few days unless a pregnancy has begun. A new corpus luteum forms every time a woman ovulates

---

[1] Togas Tulandi, MD, Haya M Al-Fozan, MD. **Recurrent pregnancy loss: Definition and etiology.** UpToDate Inc. 06Apr2022. https://www.uptodate.com (accessed on May 14, 2022).

and breaks down when it is no longer needed (monthly, until she gets pregnant). The portion of a woman's menstrual cycle in which the corpus luteum is formed is called the luteal phase. The luteal phase begins after ovulation (after an egg is released). During the luteal phase, the corpus luteum is produced, and it produces progesterone. Progesterone is required in order for the lining of the uterus to get thicker to prepare for pregnancy. If an egg is not fertilized, the corpus luteum breaks down, progesterone levels decrease, and women shed the thickened lining by having a menstrual period. The corpus luteum is required for the uterus to make the changes required for a fertilized egg to become a fetus. It has been hypothesized that a dysfunctional corpus luteum can be a potential cause of impaired progesterone production resulting in infertility or pregnancy failure. Unfortunately, it is controversial as to whether this condition really exists and is related to miscarriage. There is also no consensus on the best method to test for the condition.

If your body does not properly produce progesterone, you could have a perfectly viable, healthy baby and lose it! Progesterone is required for a successful pregnancy—period. The placenta does not form until approximately week twelve of a pregnancy. After the placenta forms, the placenta takes over sustaining the pregnancy. That means almost the entire first trimester is dependent upon progesterone.

I am so extremely thankful for our physician because while medicine is a science, the practice of medicine is an art, and God gave us the best doctor during our trial that we could have ever asked for. She practiced her art skillfully with us. I say this because she was not a pushover by any means. She said no to quite a few of our requests (rightfully so), but she said yes and appeared extremely knowledgeable when it really mattered.

When we shared our suspicions with our obstetrician, she seemed well versed in the subject and, without seeming to miss a beat, recommended we obtain a twenty-one-day progesterone level. She knew we were already using ovulation kits during our journey to parenthood, and we had been sharing our ovulation and menstruation data with her for months. She also still followed the standards of medicine and conducted the routine recurrent miscarriage workup on me and my husband. I expected that portion of the workup to return normal, and it did. I think she may have expected the same.

On May 24, 2015, my twenty-one-day progesterone level returned at 1.41ng/mL. The normal range is expected to be 6–25ng/mL. She diagnosed my progesterone level as non-ovulatory, so we started a trial of vaginal progesterone supplementation. She instructed me to notify her as soon as I got pregnant, and she would ensure a standing order was in place for a first trimester progesterone level.

For me, this meant that my miscarriages were likely *not* because the babies' constitutions were not compatible with life (which is what is commonly thought to be a cause of early spontaneous miscarriage) but because of a fixable issue! My babies were likely preventable deaths! The revelation was horrifying and joyous at the same time. I could never bring back my first two babies, but this knowledge could hopefully help us realize the dream of having children.

I got my third positive pregnancy test on June 21, 2015, only one menstrual cycle after starting the vaginal progesterone. I immediately called our doctor. Just as promised, she ordered the progesterone level, and I immediately went in to obtain the lab. The result returned later that same day. Even with the progesterone supplementation she had prescribed, my progesterone level was 8.14ng/mL. The normal range for a first trimester pregnancy is 9.3–33ng/mL. We continued progesterone supplementation for the remainder of the first trimester. Please note Progesterone is a prescription medication. I continued the supplemental progesterone through week thirteen of my pregnancy. Guess what! We did not miscarry! We gave birth to our wonderful baby, Gabriel, in February 2016.

In 2017 we found out we were pregnant again! This time was not planned, and I was not on supplemental progesterone. I immediately notified our physician. She ordered a progesterone level. It returned even lower than our first pregnancy at 5.8ng/mL. (Again the normal range for a first trimester pregnancy is 9.3-33ng/mL.) I was restarted on progesterone vaginal suppositories until week thirteen of our pregnancy. We had a second successful pregnancy! We gave birth to our beautiful baby, Sarah, in 2018.

In 2019 we found out we were pregnant for the fifth time. We again notified our physician. Progesterone levels were obtained and found to be on the lower end of normal at 11.3ng/mL, and for the third time, I was started on vaginal progesterone suppositories. We welcomed our amazing baby, Daniel, in 2020, just weeks before our country shut down due to the coronavirus. You may have noticed that for this fifth pregnancy, the progesterone was actually within normal limits. Because of my history of miscarriages due to progesterone deficiency and the fact that the progesterone was still in the lower limits of normal, they decided to supplement. I know you are wondering, did I ask for them to supplement? No, I did not, but I am glad they made that decision. I honestly do not know if I would have requested progesterone supplementation if they had made the decision not to supplement in my final pregnancy.

Let me pause here. I have titled this book *The Luteal Phase Defect*. However, I understand my diagnosis was actually "progesterone deficiency" of uncertain etiology. The truth is, even if we stop at the level of progesterone deficiency, this also is not commonly viewed as a reason for early first trimester miscarriage. When spoken of in the medical literature I found, if progesterone supplementation occurs, it is usually initiated after the first trimester! The only early pregnancy use for supplemental progesterone I found in medical literature is for intrauterine insemination. My physician used intrauterine insemination practices to dose my progesterone supplementation for luteal support after ovulation. Interestingly enough, studies have shown that progesterone supplementation for luteal support after ovulation induction/intrauterine insemination have found a higher live birth rate.

Let's look at some logistics here. At the time of writing this book, the cost of a blood pregnancy test (HCG) ranges, on average, from $27 to $56. The cost of a complete blood count (a part of standard prenatal care) ranges, on average, from $25 to $140. The cost of a blood progesterone level ranges, on average, from $31 to $104. What about the cost to treat my progesterone deficiency? According to an online search at the time I am writing this book, 100mg Progesterone tablets cost between $10.39 and $27.09 for thirty tablets.

As a comparison, a common medication used for infertility is Clomid. The average cost for 50mg Clomid tablets is $23.82 to $194 for thirty tablets. Why is this information important? From my personal experience, the process to diagnose and treat my progesterone deficiency was more cost efficient and more time efficient than other more traditional recurrent miscarriage or infertility protocols.

For practitioners, you may have noticed that our physician successfully diagnosed and treated this condition that we as a profession disagree about the existence of. I am so thankful she did. I am so glad she took a chance on investigating even the smallest possibility that I could be suffering from this "uncertain" condition. I am so thankful she thought out of the box and chose the simplest method to diagnose my disorder. I do not believe my physician was the first to treat my condition in this manner. Remember all of those chat rooms that led me to the diagnosis? I believe there are likely pockets of physicians or scattered individual physicians treating women for progesterone deficiency in this manner. The problem is, as a practicing physician, I could not obtain this information in our standard medical sources of information. I had to obtain it from other patients.

As a physician, the realization that this condition could be affecting my patients and I had no knowledge of it was upsetting. What if a woman had come to me with the same suspicions? I would not have known what steps to take. Family medicine physicians treat infertility. I am a family medicine physician. I understand further research needs to be conducted, but what if progesterone deficiency really is as simple to diagnose as a quick blood test conducted after a first miscarriage? What if it really does only require progesterone vaginal suppositories during the first trimester of pregnancy to treat this condition? My husband asked me, "What could it hurt to look at progesterone levels after a miscarriage?" Right now, I do not see any negatives to evaluating progesterone levels after a miscarriage. However, my only case to reference is my own, in which the cost was nominal, the time was negligible, and the information obtained and outcome were phenomenal. Therefore, further research is needed to provide a more scientific answer.

After my experience, I had the choice to go back to those same online chat groups and share my story, but would my physician colleagues see it? Would my peers in family medicine know that we may be missing the opportunity to help so many more of the patients we see? So, my dear colleagues, that is the reason this book is addressed to both women suffering after a miscarriage and physicians. My hope is to push this conversation and prompt more research and clinical trials so that the medical community can better address progesterone deficiency in women that have suffered a miscarriage. I am not the only woman who has suffered from this condition. I just happen to also be a physician who suffers from this condition and who may also need to treat other women who suffer from this condition. I would like the medical literature and resources that I need to be present and available if and when that day comes. Our credo is "Do no harm." Is the lack of knowledge of this condition potentially leading to women sustaining multiple unnecessary miscarriages doing harm? From my story alone, you can see that the mental, physical, emotional, and spiritual harm can be significant.

It is easy to tell women miscarriages are normal and expected. It is easy to diagnose and treat conditions already well documented with well-laid-out treatment protocols. However, the wonderful thing about being physicians is that we are investigators of the human body. We search. We hunt. We look for and follow clues. We latch on to case studies such as mine and explore the possibilities. We have been unwavering in this pursuit to identify and treat disease and illness, and I am confident that our current generation is and will continue in the same manner.

Possible Genetic Component?

Interestingly enough, since my ordeal, other women in my family have suffered early first trimester miscarriages. Is there a genetic component? I looked backward in my family tree for trends. I already knew my mother's side of the family had a very robust reproduction history, so I focused on my father's side of the family. I conducted interviews with some of the women in my family for some insight into the reproductive history of the females in the previous two generations. For the purposes of privacy, I am not publishing the miscarriage information for family members in my generation who have suffered a miscarriage. However, their miscarriages are recorded in my personal data as data for a potential genetic component. My grandmother, who had seven live births, had four sisters. Of the five women, all were married, yet only two successfully conceived. I have provided a little more detail for each woman below.

Paternal great-aunt – Married, two known early miscarriages. We do not know if she had additional pregnancies.

Paternal great-aunt – Married, no known full-term pregnancies or children. We do not know if she suffered any miscarriages.

Paternal great-aunt – Married, no known full-term pregnancies or children. We do not know if she suffered any miscarriages.

Paternal aunt – One known early miscarriage, no known full-term pregnancies or children. We do not know if she had additional pregnancies.

As a scientist, I love data. I understand we need more data in this area. I've shared my story to hopefully help women and the medical field obtain more information about this diagnosis. Based on my five pregnancies—two failed without supplemental progesterone and three successful with supplemental progesterone—I hypothesize that the luteal phase defect and progesterone deficiency is a cause of recurrent miscarriage. I hypothesize that it can be treated with supplemental progesterone during the first trimester. My story may help so many other hurting women that have come to us searching for answers, begging us to help them. I have been that desperate woman. I am so grateful God answered my prayers with a diagnosis and treatment. This could be the answer to so many other women's prayers as well.

Faith Corner

Prayer for Medical Providers:

Heavenly Father,

Thank you for allowing me to be in a community and profession that continues to grow, change, and improve. Thank you for allowing me to be one of those on the frontline of change that matters. Please continue to give me the passion, drive, and curiosity that it takes to drive this field forward every day. Give me wise ideas, inventions, and therapies that will revolutionize and change the way we do medicine. Let me be one of the ones who make an everlasting impression in medicine, whether it is a global impact or with the patients I see every day. I glorify you and thank you for your faithfulness, grace, and power in my life. It is in your name I pray.

Amen

Prayer for Women:

Dear Lord,

I glorify you now knowing that you are the all-knowing God. You know the end before the beginning. You knew me before I was formed in my mother's womb. You know my children before they are formed in my womb. I thank you that you have a plan for my life and my children's lives and that my life will be a testimony that will bring deliverance, peace, and growth to others; but most importantly, I thank you that it will bring people into a relationship with you. I thank you that you give us beauty for ashes and the oil of joy for mourning. I glorify you that I am still here. I am here, and as long as I have breath in my lungs, I will fight for you. And I know that with you, I will not lose. I glorify you even now for the victory. Victory over my pain. Victory over my sorrow. Victory over my miscarriages. I proclaim that I will be a mother. I put my hand in your hand. You have promised that I will *not* be disappointed. I am holding you to that promise, God, and I glorify you now that I will *not* be disappointed in my journey to motherhood! I lift up my physicians. I ask that you anoint their minds, anoint their hands, anoint their tongues as they minister to me in the area of my health. Let them put on the mind of Christ that they will bring forth and present every medical treatment and technique that you have ordained to be used during my road to motherhood. I glorify you now for the wise inventions, treatments, and techniques that will be used for my benefit and your glory. It is in your name I pray.

Amen!

Key Scriptures:

Isaiah 61:1–3

The Spirit of the Lord GOD is upon me; because the LORD hath anointed me to preach good tidings unto the meek; he hath sent me to bind up the brokenhearted, to proclaim liberty to the captives, and the opening of the prison to them that are bound; To proclaim the acceptable year of the LORD, and the day of vengeance of our God; to comfort all that mourn; To appoint unto them that mourn in Zion, to give unto them beauty for ashes, the oil of joy for mourning, the garment of praise for the spirit of heaviness; that they might be called trees of righteousness, the planting of the LORD, that he might be glorified.

Psalm 126:5–6

They that sow in tears shall reap in joy. He that goeth forth and weepeth, bearing precious seed, shall doubtless come again with rejoicing, bringing his sheaves with him.

Genesis 21:2

For Sarah conceived, and bare Abraham a son in his old age, at the set time of which God has spoken.

Jeremiah 29:11

For I know the thoughts that I think toward you, saith the LORD, thoughts of peace, and not of evil, to give you an expected end.

Isaiah 55:8–9

For my thoughts are not your thoughts, neither are your ways, my ways, declares the Lord. For as the heavens are higher than the earth, so are my ways higher than your ways, and my thoughts than your thoughts.

Hebrews 10:35–39

Cast not away therefore your confidence, which has great recompense of good reward. For ye have need of patience, that after ye have done the will of God, ye might receive the promise. For yet a little while, and he that shall come will come, and will not tarry. Now the just shall live by faith: but if any man draw back, my soul shall have no pleasure in him. But we are not of them who draw back unto perdition; but of them that believe to the saving of the soul.

This final scripture was the one that I recited over and over every day until I held our first son. I still have it as my screensaver on my phone. I pray this is a blessing to all women seeking motherhood.

Isaiah 49:23b

Then you will know that I am the LORD; those who hope in me will not be disappointed.

Epilogue

Pregnancy After a Miscarriage (or Two)

I got my third positive pregnancy test on June 21, 2015. Hooray! I was pregnant, I was elated, I was overjoyed, and...I was terrified of miscarrying again. I knew God did not give me a spirit of fear. I needed help to overcome my fear of miscarriage, even after we survived the first trimester. I actually felt secure during the first trimester while I was taking the progesterone, and I was extremely fearful when the time came to stop the supplements.

I knew God did not want me living in fear and that He wanted me to enjoy and thrive during my pregnancy, but I needed tools. I didn't have the time or energy to pore through the Bible finding scriptures for my situation. I am so thankful that I found three books that helped get me through my third pregnancy: *Supernatural Childbirth* by Jackie Mize, *Prayers and Promises for Supernatural Childbirth* also by Jackie Mize, and *Praying Through Your Pregnancy* by Jennifer Polimino and Caroyln Warren. I love the Word of God, and nothing delivers like the Word of God. These books provided biblical scriptures that I recited every time doubt, fear, or any negative thought entered my mind. Many times I recited these scriptures multiple times a day. Why do I refer to these books here? Well, the purpose of my book is to provide godly encouragement to hurting parents after a miscarriage and additional education to the medical community about a possible cause of recurrent miscarriage that is currently not widely accepted. I do not want to reinvent the wheel. The resources I'm listing here are anointed and were a gift from God in my life. If you need them, I pray they will be a blessing to you during your journey to motherhood as well.

How did my daily faith walk look? Every day was different, but there was lots and lots of prayer. I literally opened my eyes—maybe...I sometimes just realized I was awake—and started to pray before I even opened my eyes. I thanked God for another day and asked Him to watch over me that day. Basic, right? But even that little action is training your mind to stay focused on God. Isaiah 26:3 says, "Thou wilt keep him in perfect peace, whose mind is stayed on thee: because he trusteth in thee." I was building my trust in God in this new uncharted territory.

I had some key scriptures that I printed and posted in my bedroom and bathroom and saved some as screenshots in my phone. I read these almost every morning, sometimes multiple times a day if I needed a pick-me-up. If doubt or any negative thought or fear tried to arise, I immediately cast it down with prayer and scripture. The thoughts definitely came. If I didn't feel the baby moving for a while, the thoughts would try to creep in. I knew I needed to cast down every imagination. Second Corinthians 10:5 says, "Casting down imaginations, and every high thing that exalteth itself against the knowledge of God, and bringing into captivity every thought to the obedience of Christ." It actually became a "thing" during pregnancy, where I would get nervous if Gabriel didn't move for a while. I would pray and then ask God to let me feel the baby move. Like clockwork, Gabriel would give one kick, as if to say, "I'm good, Mom. Go back to sleep." I would tell the Lord thank you for humoring me and go back to sleep. He is a faithful God even when our faith is weak. I am so glad my God was and still is patient with me. He is

47

a patient father.

At the beginning of my pregnancy, my prayers were short and sweet. By the end of my pregnancy, I had so much scripture marinating in my spirit that my morning prayers seemed to last most of the morning. I would start while I was lying in bed but continue as I went about my morning routine. I might pause while I contemplated what I was going to wear or looked for my favorite socks, but then I would pick right back up. Anything that plagued me in the previous day or weeks I would cast down before it could plague me again, and to be honest, new negative thoughts tried to creep in for the duration of that pregnancy. There was a lot of prayer!

It got to the point where a thought would start, a scripture would come to my spirit, I would pray that scripture as it related to me, and I would then keep going with whatever activity I was doing. They were quick, short moments that other people wouldn't even notice. I might be standing in line at a movie waiting for my husband to get my large pretzel with cheese. A negative thought would come then a scripture and a prayer. I'd grab my pretzel and enjoy the movie. Sometimes it was as simple as saying, "I will not be disappointed. Daddy, I thank you that you are taking care of this pregnancy. I am in your hands. I trust you when you said I will not be disappointed. I am blessed and highly favored. Glory, glory to your name." Instead of the common phrase, "I've got a pill for that," I was operating in "I've got a scripture/prayer for that!" Jude 20 says, "But ye, beloved, building up yourselves on your most holy faith, praying in the Holy Ghost." Now, I believe in praying in the Holy Ghost through the evidence of speaking in tongues, and I most definitely pray and speak in tongues. However, I will say praying in your natural language and your own understanding also builds your faith. Take advantage of God through both avenues.

I also refused to listen to or watch anything that would allow negative thoughts to enter my mind. I surrounded myself with only things that would build my faith. I remember when I was having a hard time passing my USMLE exams, someone close to me asked, "What will you do if you don't pass this last time?" I abruptly ended the conversation and did not talk to that person again until after I passed my tests. Now, that person was not malicious. I love that person dearly. Of course that question was in the back of my head, but I was working hard to cast it down and only speaking that I would pass. When my faith is weak in an area in which I am believing for a miracle or a breakthrough, I can't allow my faith to be influenced by anything that will make it weaker.

Again, God taught me this lesson before the fight of my life, so I applied it without remorse during my pregnancy. No one asked me what I would do if I miscarried again, but I also stayed away from any situation that had the potential to lead down that path. I stayed away from voices that could potentially ask those sorts of questions. If I was around people, I surrounded myself with people of faith who spoke life into me and my situation without solicitation. I had people speaking such wonderful, life-giving, encouraging words to me; it was amazing. I just chose those people carefully. I listened only to music that spoke life, encouragement, and faith to me. I watched TV and movies that did the same. I built my faith in everything that I did. I surrounded and covered myself with God's Word, prayer, and faith.

Dear reader, I am so thankful that you have taken the time to share in my testimony, and I pray that you have been blessed and encouraged. For mothers who have suffered a miscarriage, God sees. He knows. He cares. He is faithful. He is a healer. He is the God of the miraculous. He is all you need. He is the answerer of prayers. He hears your prayers, and I know He will answer your prayers and that you will not be disappointed. Though it may be the path less traveled, I pray God's blessings over you on your journey to motherhood!

Faith Corner

Prayer for Women:

Heavenly Father,

Thank you so much for an opportunity to hear your heart toward me. Your word says in Jeremiah 29:11–12, "'For I know the plans I have for you', declares the LORD, 'plans to prosper you and not to harm you, plans to give you hope and a future. Then you will call on me and come and pray to me, and I will listen to you.'" Thank you for reminding me of your love, power, and plans for my life. Thank you for these seeds of hope in my spirit. Thank you for being the ultimate doctor who can heal any wound and calm every fear. Thank you for showing me where my help comes from. According to Psalm 121:1–2, "I will lift up mine eyes to the hills, from whence cometh my help. My help cometh from the Lord, which made heaven and earth." Help me to keep my eyes on you. You are the way, the truth, and the life. I will believe what your Word says about me, and I will walk in the faith and knowledge that my heavenly Father is in control, that He has all power in His hands, and that He will never leave me nor forsake me. I know this to be true and declare that I will walk in this knowledge daily. I speak blessings over my body, my womb, my mind, my spirit. I speak blessings over your most precious daughter, ME! I glorify you now for the blessings you have in store for me! I come in agreement with you and claim them even now. I give you all of the glory, honor, and praise! It is in your holy and matchless name I pray! Amen

Key Scriptures:

Exodus 23:25–26

And ye shall serve the LORD your God, and he shall bless thy bread, and thy water; and I will take sickness away from the midst of thee. There shall nothing cast their young, nor be barren, in thy land: the number of thy days I will fulfil.

Deuteronomy 7:13

And he will love thee, and bless thee, and multiply thee: he will also bless the fruit of thy womb, and the fruit of thy land, thy corn, and thy wine, and thine oil, the increase of thy kine, and the flocks of thy sheep, in the land which he sware unto thy fathers to give thee.

Faith Scriptures

These are just a few more of the scriptures that I recited over and over as I rebuilt my faith, trust, hope, and expectancy in my faithful Lord and Savior. God's Word is sufficient. I am nothing if not a child of God. I pray these scriptures bless you.

1 Samuel 1:27

For this child I prayed; and the LORD hath given me my petition which I asked of him.

Psalm 113:9

He maketh the barren woman to keep house, and to be a joyful mother of children. Praise ye the LORD.

Hebrews 11:6

For without faith it is impossible to please him: for he that cometh to God must believe that he is, and that he is a rewarder of them that diligently seek him.

Luke 1:37

For with God nothing shall be impossible.

3 John 2

Beloved, I wish above all things that thou mayest prosper and be in health, even as thy soul prospereth.

Isaiah 53:4–5

But he was wounded for our transgressions, he was bruised for our iniquities; the chastisement of our peace is upon him and with his stripes we are healed.

Isaiah 54:17

No weapon formed against me shall prosper.

Habakkuk 2:3

For the vision is yet for an appointed time, but at the end it shall speak, and not lie: though it tarry, wait for it; because it will surely come, it will not tarry.

John 7:38

He that believeth on me, as the scripture hath said, out of his belly shall flow rivers of living water.

Romans 8:28

And we know that all things work together for good to them that love God, to them who are the called according to his purpose.

About the Author

Joni Stuart Cazeau, MD, is a wife, mother, Family Medicine physician, U.S Navy veteran, and a child of God. She is married to her husband, Jean Cazeau. The two have three children, Gabriel, Ellise, and Daniel. Joni began her journey as a published author cowriting a children's book series with her own children, Gabriel and Ellise. Jean serves as the illustrator for the family's children's book series. The baby of the family, Daniel, has a book series titled after his name as well. Joni lives with her family in Rhode Island with their dog, Cazmic.

Printed in Great Britain
by Amazon

46353478R00036